Ge

Lanz

CW00923478

by

ISBN 0 900717 74 2

CONTENTS

PREFACE

Lanzarote, a holiday island destination for hundreds of thousands of visitors each year, is located about 150 km from the coast of Morocco. It is the most easterly island of the Canary Islands Archipelago, a chain of dormant volcanoes about 600 km long stretching out into the North Atlantic Ocean. Volcanic activity commenced about 40-50 million years ago. Along its northeast-southwest axis Lanzarote extends for 59 km and it width varies from 8 km in the north, where the highest point occurs at Peñas del Cache (670m) to about 20 km in the central area. The combination of ease of access, abundant accommodation, good metalled roads, short distances of travel to exposures and, above all, a welcoming sunny climate throughout most of the year means that it is the absolutely ideal place for a leisurely study of volcanic activity. Temperatures range between 14-21°C in winter and 18-28°C in summer, often ameliorated by strong sea breezes. Rainfall is about 140mm per year on average and contributes to the growth of wild plants such as the ice plant *Mesembryanthemum*, *Limonium*, storks's bill *Erodium* and poppies. The northern Famara part of the island is the wettest and shows the most prolific growth, particularly of species of *Euphorbia*.

For such a relatively small island (797 square km) the scenery is spectacular in many places. It is no surprise that certain areas have been declared to be National Parks or Protected Areas, as at Timanfaya in the west and around the Malpais de la Corona and the Casa de Los Volcánes (Jameos del Agua) in the north. In 1993 UNESCO designated Lanzarote as a *World Biosphere Site* in recognition of its natural environments.

This guide is intended for those who are intrigued by the various manifestations of volcanicity, either via television programmes, videos or books, and who wish to experience first hand the consequences of such without having to trek long distances in dangerous terrain. Although geological technicalities have to be introduced these are kept to a minimum and a glossary is incorporated.

Topographical and road maps for Lanzarote are easy to come by, being sold in many shops and resorts on the island, but the AA - Macmillan *Canary Islands Travellers Map*, available in Britain, is quite adequate at a scale of 1:200,000. In Lanzarote itself there is the English edition of the *Map of Lanzarote* published by Yaiza S.L. at a better scale of 1:100,000 and ideal for location purposes. A rather splendid *Geographical/Volcanic Map for Lanzarote* is produced by Editiones A.M. again at a scale of 1:100,000. The last includes a good geological map of the solid rocks, a modification of which occurs in this guide (Figure 2). In certain shops in 1998-99 there also appeared an excellent satellite photograph of the whole island, and Graciosa to the north, at a scale of 1:62,500. To cap it all, there is now available a satellite-based map on the same scale of 1:62,500 on which nearly all of the

(iii)

volcanoes, roads, towns and villages are clearly named.

The only satisfactory way of visiting not only the rocks of the island but also various spectacular viewpoints (miradors), museums and important places associated with the noted artist and designer César Manrique, is to hire an ordinary car, easily accomplished at all major resorts.   Local bus transport is very restricted in terms of routes and is somewhat irregular in frequency. The main roads are designated LZ and the driving is on the right.

All the locations in this guide are either roadside or involve walking short distances along tracks.   None involve the hazardous crossing of the surface of lava flows or such-like, which requires heavy-duty footwear and other protective clothing. Parking is no problem except within the boundaries of the National Parks where there are, nonetheless, specific parking areas. **In the National Parks the collecting of specimens is not allowed.**

I am very pleased to acknowledge the cartographic expertise of Colin Stuart in drawing the first four figures of this guide.   Expenses were defrayed from a specific legacy to the Geologists' Association left by John Eric Farnaby.   I am especially indebted to my wife, Pat, for her acute geological observations and photographic work in the field, and in checking the numerous versions of the text.   The Curry Fund generously covered the printing costs.

LIST OF FIGURES

Page

GEOLOGICAL HISTORY

The Canary Islands are situated in the northwestern part of the African Plate, well away from the Mid-Atlantic Ridge to the west which is a constructive plate boundary, but not too far distant from the boundary with the major Euro-Asian Plate to the north (Figure 1). They occupy a transitional zone, a passive continental margin, between oceanic and continental crust. The northern plate boundary, which roughly extends west-east from the Azores into the eastern Mediterranean Sea, is partly of the nature of a transform fault zone. Along a considerable length of the zone, which extends for about 2750 km, the plates are intermittently slipping

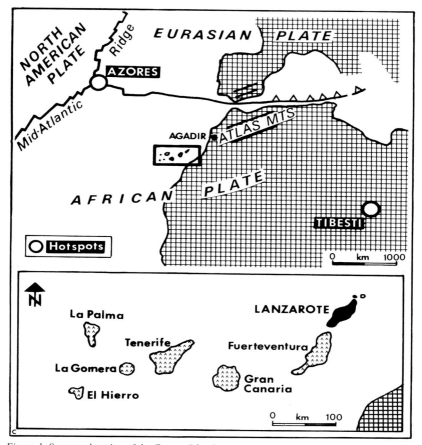

Figure 1. Structural setting of the Canary Islands

Geological History

sideways by each other. The volcanicity in the Canaries seems to be associated with fracture zones of distension and compression in the sub-surface which run obliquely towards the transform plate boundary and may well have been activated or re-activated by movements along it in early to mid-Eocene and Miocene times. The fracture zones in Lanzarote, mainly trending WSW-ENE, but some SSW-NNE, appear to be seawards extensions from similar trending structures in the Atlas Mountain ranges, which abut the transform. A significant episode of the Alpine Orogeny, some 20 million years ago in the Miocene epoch, seems to have caused an upheaval of the Atlas Mountains and initiated the first major *sub-aerial* phase of volcanicity in Lanzarote, more or less simultaneously.

The mainland and island faults still show varying degrees of activity, sometimes in the form of disastrous earthquakes as at Agadir in Morocco in 1960, when 12,000 inhabitants died. But the seismicity of Lanzarote, though frequent, is of relatively low magnitude (1.2-2) at present, with hypocentres located at depths varying between 500 metres and 26 kilometres. Most of the minor earth tremors probably originate by geothermal activity resulting from the interaction of ascending magma with groundwater near to the surface, as at Timanfaya, or sea-water as once was the case at El Golfo.

It is important to appreciate that the fractures and faults have acted intermittently as conduits for the ascent of basic magma emanating from the crust or mantle.

Many years ago (Wilson 1963; Hoernle & Schminke, 1993) it was suggested that the volcanicity of the Canary Islands was caused by them being located over a deep-seated source of heat in the mantle, 70 km or more down. The heat being transported upwards in the form of a concentrated plume or convection current ("hot spot"), melting the foundation rocks and creating magma on the way. This might well have been the case at some earlier stage in the history - "hot spots" do decay - but since the suggestion was made it has been deduced that there is no such thing at present underneath the islands. The nearest being located beneath the Azores, Cape Verde Islands and, somewhat surprisingly, the Tibesti Uplift on the Libya - Chad border. Moreover, the Canaries rocks differ in petrological detail from those associated with mid-oceanic and oceanic "hot spots". They are generally more sodium-rich, moderately undersaturated and more allied to a continental situation. They belong predominantly to the alkaline magma series and are dominated by alkali basalts.

Geophysical surveys strongly suggest that immediately beneath the bottom of the Lanzarote volcanic pile there is mainly a succession of mixed sedimentary strata akin to that of the marginal basins around the northwest African coast. Some of the sedimentary rocks are probably Palaeocene even Cretaceous in age, a deduction based on the identification of marine microfossils in limestone fragments found in the ash deposits of the much degraded Pico del Cuchillo caldera (Pleistocene), in the north of the Central Plain.

The cores of some basaltic rocks and bombs at this locality and elsewhere consist of enclaves of dunite (an ultrabasic olivine-dominated rock) and gabbro. These coarser grained rocks have clearly been derived from greater depths below the sedimentary basement, possibly from the mantle some 15 or so kilometres down.

It is interesting that, during all these volcanic events, real or hypothetical, there was no significant mineralisation of prospective major economic value, of the rocks in Lanzarote, or elsewhere in the Canaries for that matter.

Date	Sequence	Formation
1824 AD	Holocene	Last eruptions
1730-36 AD	Holocene	Timanfaya Group
3000-1000 BC	Holocene	Corona Group
10,000 years		
	Upper - Middle Pleistocene	Central Areas, Rubicon
700,000 years		
	Lower Pleistocene	Teguise Group, Playa Blanca
1.6 m.y.		
2 m.y. gap		
3.8 m.y.		
	Mio-Pliocene	Famara Group
5.7-6.5m.y. Upper Miocene Tias Formation		
10.2 m.y.		
3 m.y. gap		
13.5 m.y.		
	Middle Miocene	Ajaches Formation
14.5 m.y.		

Table 1. Volcanic succession in Lanzarote

Geological History

Probably the greatest problem that the earliest workers met on this and the other Canary Islands was working out the stratigraphy of the volcanic episodes in the general absence of fossil-bearing sequences of strata.   At some localities it is possible to see younger lavas wrapping themselves around older volcanic cones. Some volcanic sequences are clearly more strongly weathered and carry thicker superficial layers of caliche (see p. 6), or are less well vegetated than others, all useful distinguishing characteristics for establishing relative age over very restricted areas.   For the youngest sequences there is also good historical evidence.   Over larger regions, however, something more satisfactory was required and in the last few decades a certain amount of work on the geomagnetic polarity and radiometric dating

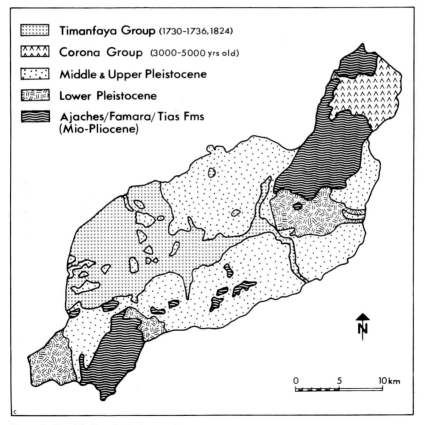

Figure 2. Simplified geological map of Lanzarote.
  (After Carracedo & Rodríguez Badiola, 1993)

of the succession has taken place (Abdel-Monem *et al*, 1971; Araña & Carracedo, 1978). This work has established broad age patterns for the Miocene, Pliocene and Pleistocene deposits.

The oldest basaltic volcanic rocks of the Canaries, known as the Basement Complex, are not exposed on Lanzarote and are at least early Miocene in age. However, deep borehole evidence suggests that some form of volcanicity probably commenced as early as Eocene times, about 40-50 million years ago. The oldest exposed volcanics, the Ajaches Formation that is at least 300 metres thick, occur in the topographically prominent Los Ajaches range and in other small inliers (e.g. Salinas del Janubio) in the southwest of the island and have ages given as 14.5 to 13.5 m.y. This age range puts them into the middle part of the Miocene epoch (Figure 2). They are characterised by being shot through by basic dykes.

Another old elevated mass formed by the Famara Formation is at the northern end of Lanzarote. It forms the foundation of the spectacular westwards facing Famara cliffs (El Risco and El Risco de Famara) that are about 20 kilometres long. The lower part of this formation appears to have a Miocene age varying between 10.2 and 8.7 m.y. There appears to be general agreement that there was a period of volcanic quiescence between the final emission of the Ajaches volcanics and the beginning of the Famara emissions, maybe lasting as much as 3 million years according to some, half a million years according to others.

The sequence exposed in the Famara cliffs, however, is more complex than it appears. There seem to have been at least three superimposed cycles of eruption separated by long intervals of time, up to at least 2 million years, when activity ceased or markedly diminished. The Lower Famara Formation 10.2 - 8.7 m.y. and the Middle Famara Formation 6.5 - 5.7 m.y. are both Miocene in age and the Upper Famara Formation 3.9 - 3.8 m.y. is Pliocene. A certain amount of overspill of lavas occurred much later, some 3000-5000 years ago associated with renewed activity in the Volcán de la Corona area (Locality 3; Figure 7).

It is of some significance that the alignment of the volcanic centres in both the Ajaches and Famara masses is approximately north-northeast - south-southwest. This is indicative of the alignment of major fractures or fissures in the subsurface at the time allowing easier access for the ascending basic magmas. The bulk of the volcanic eruptions in Lanzarote, through to more recent times, has been controlled by the orientation of such fissures.

Both the Ajaches and Famara successions have been subject to intensive erosion, some marine, some subaerial, during subsequent oscillations in sea-level commencing in late-Miocene times and extending through into Pliocene and Quaternary times. As a consequence their topography is well rounded and mature compared with elsewhere on the island. A characteristic morphological feature inland indicative of subaerial erosive phases are valleys (or barrancos), some deep and gorge-like, others flat-bottomed and broad. These are well seen on the flanks of both of the old masses. The west-facing flanks, in addition, are typified by large, sometimes interlocking, subaerial fans of scree, composed of volcanic debris. They are particularly well-developed in the Ajaches range to the east of Playa Blanca (Locality 14) and also mantle the foot of the Famara cliffs (Locality 3).

Another feature of these oldest volcanic terrains has been the progressive development on their surfaces of reddened ferruginous soil profiles (rubefaction), sometimes as much as 10 metres thick, as at Mirador del Río (Locality 3) in the north. Good thick exposures also occur at intervals along the roadside (LZ-10) between Haría and Teguise, and on the flanks of Guanapay (Locality 11). The build-up of these soils on the heights reflects the long periods available, from the late Miocene and Pliocene onwards, for subaerial weathering to take place. This situation contrasts with more recent lava flows and ashes, where soils are virtually non-existent. Unsurprisingly, around the margins of the old masses, the relatively fertile soil tends to wash down the slopes and the barrancos into lower-lying areas creating horticultural conditions suitable for the growth of cereals (maize, etc), fruits (almonds, etc) and legumes (peas, beans, lentils, etc).

While dealing with soils and soil processes it is worth mentioning the widespead development of caliche-profiles, not only affecting the surface of the oldest volcanics but also some of the younger, though not too obviously in the most recent, that is those erupted over the last 300 years or so. Caliche is a crust-like accumulation of creamy-white calcite forming layers anything up to 5 metres thick, as near to Mojón (Locality 7), some quite hard but generally soft and friable. The calcite is precipitated from ground water rich in calcium (derived from the weathering of the underlying ashes and lavas) being pulled towards the surface during drier seasonal phases - a kind of capillary movement. The precipitated calcite progressively fills the spaces between the volcanic minerals and grains, and ultimately replaces some of the original materials.

The Tias Formation of Upper Miocene basaltic lavas lavas shot through with dykes occurs as a string of small inliers, trending west-southwest - east-northeast, from the Salinas de Janubio (Locality 17) via Tias village to near the airport. They are mainly distributed along a tract of country adjacent to the LZ-2 road and, just to the east of Tias village, the lavas are actively worked for road metal and other constructional purposes in one of the very few such quarries on the island. The inliers are surrounded by Middle to Upper Pleistocene volcanics, many forming an aligned series of cones on the northern side of the LZ-2, but extending as far as Montaña Corona (235 m), near to Playa Teguise.

The next major period of volcanicity following the Mio-Pliocene episodes occurred in Lower Pleistocene times, commencing about 1.6 million years ago. It is reflected in two main areas of outcrop according to Carracedo and Rodriguez Badiola (1993), one occupying a large tract to the east of Teguise and the other extending southwards from Playa de Janubio to Playa Blanca. However, it needs to be mentioned that other workers would extend the outcrops of the Lower Pleistocene to cover most of the Central Plain (see Henar Barreiro, 1995, 1:100,000 Volcanic Map on sale in most shops on the island). There are relatively few volcanoes to be seen associated with this period of activity and those that are present show their age by being considerably eroded. Pico del Cuchillo (Peak of the Knife) (Locality 13), 3 kilometres inland from La Costa is one such, as is Montaña Roja (Red Mountain), 2.5 kilometres west of Playa Blanca.

The Central Plain has extensive lava and ash fields that are taken in this guide to be mainly Middle to Upper Pleistocene in age. It is intriguing that these are mantled in places by a thin veneer of younger wind-blown beach and coastal sand, probably Holocene in part. Parts of this comparatively low-lying but rolling terrain are referred to as El Jable. The sands are well-exposed adjacent to the roadsides, especially in the north, and give large areas a desert-like appearance. This pale yellow, almost white, sand clearly has been transported inland for many thousands of years by the prevailing northerly trade winds. It stands out remarkably well on satellite photographs, in contrast to the darker browns, grey and blacks of most lava flows and ash deposits. Although the fertility of the sand-affected areas is poor to very moderate it is possible, using appropriate horticultural methods, to enhance its quality. In practise, this involves adding fertilizers and manure to the sand or soil, followed by a thin capping of ash, the latter helping water retention. This particular methodology can be seen at work around the margins of the Plain and adjacent to the villages. Pumpkins, water-melons, tomatoes and cereals (maize, rye, barley, etc) are the main crops.

In contrast to the Central Plain, the roughly equivalent-aged lavas and tephra deposits to the northeast of Playa Blanca, have even more poorly developed lichen-flecked light brown soils and carry thin, irregular veneers of caliche.

Outcrops of the Middle to Upper Pleistocene successions also run around the northern end of the Ajaches range at Uga before widening and extending intermittently northeastwards via Tias and Arrecife as far as Arrieta. As mentioned earlier the alignment of the marked series of volcanoes, such as Caldera Riscarda (446 m), Montana de Maneje (282 m) (Locality 10) and La Caldera (324 m) (Locality 6) is essentially along west-southwest east-northeast lines controlled by several deep-seated fracture lines in the crust. La Caldera, one of the "Guitiza Boilers" to the southeast of the LZ-1, is easily picked out as it has been worked for ash and the worked faces show a certain degree of collapse. It seems likely over this period of time that volcanicity affected most of the island and the disconnected outcrop pattern seen at present is due to a mantling by later volcanic products. This is especially the case with a number of cones and calderas, located for example in Timanfaya National Park, which are completely flanked by the extensive lava flows of 1730-1736. These inliers are referred to as "islotes", literally small barren islands. Caldera Blanca (458 m) in the National Park, called such because of a veneer of caliche, is a prime example as is the more accessible Islote de Hilario, which encompasses the El Diablo restaurant and adjacent car park (Locality 20). Visitors to the restaurant can see regular demonstrations of the natural heat emitted from "experiment tubes" bored into these Pleistocene volcanics. Added water explodes as a jet of steam as it is heated up and vegetation pushed into the tubes ignites, unsurprisingly as the temperatures reach 435° Centigrade a few metres below the surface.

The next phase of major eruptions occurred some 3000-5000 years ago at the northern end of the island and is referred to as the Corona Phase or Episode, named after the breached caldera of Volcán de la Corona (609 m) (Back cover, upper). There are several closely linked eruptive centres adjacent to la Corona aligned roughly northeast - southwest. They include the cones of La Quemeda de Orzola (356 m), just to the east of Yé, Los Helechos (581 m) and La Quemada (562 m). Lavas and tephra poured from these volcanoes, some of the former travelling westwards and dropping over the pre-existing Famara precipices (Locality 3). Most travelled eastwards and are now represented by an extensive blocky (aa) lava field - the Malpais de la Corona (the Badlands of Corona). These lavas still look remarkably fresh and practically devoid of anything remotely resembling soil, though scrubby low-lying vegetation, especially *Euphorbia* and lichens, is evident. There is a certain amount of horticulture adjacent to the main Arrieta - Yé road and vines are grown. However, there is a suspicion that at least some of these more fertile patches are likely to be caused by soils reworked down-slope from the Famara massif to the west.

The eastwards outpouring of Corona lavas covers about 50 square kilometres and widened the northern end of the island by about 5 kilometres. A remarkably preserved and accessible feature of the lava field is a volcanic tube extending from the foot of the Volcán de la Corona southeastwards into the sea near Jameos del Agua, a distance of about 8 kilometres (Figure 4 and Localities 1 & 2).

Lava tubes are relatively common in the Holocene lavas of the island. However, they are not always very apparent unless you can see the aligned depressions or pits (jameos) at the surface caused by the subsequent collapse of their roofs. One such, modified to the design of César Manrique, is now occupied by the Cactus Garden just to the north of Guatiza. The garden was opened in 1990 and contains more than 1400 species and more than 9700 individual plants of cacti and succulents.

Breached lava tubes and lava channels can also be observed during a circular guided coach tour (Ruta de los Volcánes) of the volcanic terrain of the Montañas del Fuego area (private cars are not allowed on the 14 kilometre route). But they are really a very small part of this most spectacularly volcanic part of the island, the National Park of Timanfaya, which strongly reflects the results of the next major series of fissure eruptions beginning on 1st September 1730 and continuing through until 16th April 1736. The lavas and scoria cover some 174 square kilometres, with a volume assessed as 1.3 cubic kilometres, and issued from as many as 25 craters, including over 100 individual vents with heights between 50-100 metres. Many of the craters and vents are aligned in an east-northeast - west-southwest direction. Each vent appears to have been active for about 12 days. Great and impressive tracts of the island extending as far as the coastline are mantled by the blue-black, blocky and infertile lavas making them virtually impassable by foot. Individual lava flows were anything between 4 kilometres and 12 kilometres long. Some seventeen country establishments, including eleven villages, and patches of relatively fertile soils were utterly destroyed. At one stage it looked as though the lavas would overwhelm the attractive village of Yaiza, but forward movement ceased just to the north of the village, its edge now very visible along the line of the northern bypass (Front Cover).

The southern edges of the 1730-1736 lava field can be seen at many points adjacent to the scenic Uga to Masdache road (LZ-30), through an area known as La Geria. The blocky lavas, often clearly piled one on top of another, sometimes contain spectacular accumulations of olivine (Location 22). Tongues of lava also extended southwards towards Macher and eastwards, before splitting into two arms. One of these moved northwards into the Central Plain and the other southwards around the flanks of Montaña Ubique and Montaña Maneje, via the Fundación César Manrique (Locality 9), to the edge of the sea, east of Arrecife (Locality 8).

Abutting the southern edge of the lava field in La Geria are extensive patches of contemporaneous wind-blown fine ashes, transported by the prevailing winds from the north. They tend to have a relatively higher degree of fertility and moisture-holding capacity than the lavas and are especially suitable for vine and fig tree cultivation, especially when fertilized and mantled with lapilli ash, which acts as a mulch. Usually the plants are established in man-made circular, walled depressions, just a few metres across (Figure 29). This arrangement helps to funnel rain and dew-fall towards the roots. Several commercial vineyards are located in this area.

The last significant volcanic episode in Lanzarote followed a twelve year period of earth tremors and occurred between 31st July and 24th October 1824. Along the line of an east-northeast - west-southwest trending, 13 kilometre-long fissure, three eruptions occurred, these building up into volcanoes at Tiagua (Montana del Clerigo Duarte, 301 m) and, within the National Park proper, Volcán Nuevo de Tinguatón (330 m) and Montaña del Chinero (356 m). The lava flows were not extensive.

Before leaving this potted history of the island it is worth emphasising one of the curiosities, that is the beaches and adjacent areas. Many of the popular holiday resorts have sandy beaches, albeit somewhat restricted in width, as in the patchy developments along the northern coast to the east of Orzola. But there are more extensive beaches at Punta del Papagayo, just east of las Coloradas, Puerto del Carmen and Playa de Famara. Some of the beach deposits are grey-black and pebbly, having been derived from adjacent volcanics, as at Salinas de Janubio and El Golfo (Localities 17 & 18), but others are extraordinary in being composed of light brown, almost white, sand. The latter is composed predominantly of quartz, with variable amounts of comminuted sea-shell fragments, a sprinkling of gypsum, ferro-magnesian minerals such as pyroxenes, and iron oxides. As the volcanic rocks of the island do not contain quartz, the mineral grains must have been introduced from outside sources. It is generally considered that such sources were the adjacent Northwest African coastal zone and the Saharan Desert. Subaerial transport may well have been via strong northeasterly trade winds and occasional warm easterly winds prevailing over the last few million years. On some days at present, when the easterly winds are blowing, the whole island is blanketed by a grey-brown smog of wind-blown dust. An indeterminate amount of quartz sand may also have been transported by oceanic currents from the African littoral zone, being reworked and recycled in the various shelf-like shallows during sea-level changes, but progressively moving westwards before finishing-up at Lanzarote.

Although it has to be appreciated that rises and falls in absolute sea-level must have affected the Canary Islands as a whole since at least late Miocene times, the actual physical expression of such is not too obvious, certainly at most of the localities visited in this guide. Successive eruptive events have in many cases obliterated what could have been determinative evidence. By looking round at Punta del Aguila (Locality 15) and Salinas de Janubio (Locality 17) you can see that the land surface at an altitude of about 20 metres above sea-level is naturally bevelled. This suggests a long period of raised sea-level and marine planation post-dating the affected Miocene and early Pleistocene lava successions. Possibly the marine platform (rasa) reflects a sea-level high (or highs) during mid-Pleistocene times. However, matters are complicated by the fact that volcanic terrains are capable of being physically uplifted as a consequence of active volcanicity. This process might well have played some role in what you can observe.

ASPECTS OF THE VOLCANOLOGY OF LANZAROTE

The bulk of the extrusive rocks (lavas and scoria) of Lanzarote are alkaline basaltic in character with a mild variation in mineralogy which, technically, makes some of them basanites, others picritic basalts.   Trachy-basalts, more silica-rich and some showing flow texture, are also present (Locality 16).   It is probable that all originated from the partial melting of peridotitic materials within the oceanic crust or upper mantle, followed by mild differentiation during emplacement.   You need to be quite expert with a hand-lens, or ultimately with a petrographic microscope, to distinguish between the varieties, so only a few brief notes will be made here.

The extrusives constituting the ancient Miocene Ajaches and Famara ranges are to a large degree basanites, though the former area also incorporates picritic basalts and trachy-basalts.   The basanites and picritic basalts are dark porphyritic rocks carrying phenocrysts of olivine and monoclinic pyroxenes, such as augite and diopside, set in a microcrystalline (even glassy in some instances) matrix of calcic plagioclase, pyroxenes and opaque iron/titanium oxides.   The basanites should also carry a small amount of nepheline.   The alkaline basalts, interleaved with basanites, in the younger volcanic sequences are also commonly porphyritic carrying phenocrysts of olivine and augite, some of the former being quite large.   They are set in a glassy or microcrystalline matrix of plagioclase feldspar, clino- and orthopyroxenes, plus opaques.

The bulk of the lava flows associated with the active phases of volcanicity in Lanzarote are of the aa type (slaggy, blocky-topped: a Polynesian name) and as such the upper jumbled layers are essentially autoclastic in origin.   That is, they formed by break-up at the surface of the flow as it moved downslope.   A common name for these layers, in which some of the blocks are massive, is flow-breccia.   Ropy lava (pahoehoe: another Polynesian name) can be observed at the Cesar Manrique Foundation, near Tahiche (Locality 9) and at Playa de la Arena, Arrecife (Locality 8), but is widespread on the surfaces of jumbled blocks in the extensive lava fields of the Timanfaya National Park.   When contemporary lava flows, especially of the blocky type, combine and spread out widely, often a function of the topography prevailing at the time, the lava fields which are created are referred to as malpais (badlands). Such is the Malpais de la Corona (the Badlands of the Crown) in the north of the island.

Sometimes the surface of active lava flows is disrupted explosively and small, steep-sided cones of coarse tephra are built-up.   These have a distinctive appearance and are known as hornitos.   There are several good examples visible from the El Diablo restaurant area in the National Park (Locality 20, Figure 25, Lower).

Feeder dykes for the lavas, essentially of similar composition to the lavas, can sometimes be observed, but are especially prominent in the Mio-Pliocene sequences. Some of the best exposures are in the steep sea-cliffs at Castillo de las Coloradas and roadside crags in the nearby las Coloradas village, east of Playa Blanca (Localities 15 & 16; Figures 17, 18 and 19). Many of the dykes there trend northeast - southwest, are closely spaced and occasionally multiple in type. Chilled margins can be seen clearly. Another good set of dykes occur at Salinas de Janubio (Locality 17), also trending roughly northeast - southwest and reflecting, once again, the deep-seated fracture pattern of the island.

Virtually all of the volcanic cones on the island are composed of scoria, a general term describing ash, lapilli, cinders and other slag-like material. Lava flows are usually emitted from near to the base of the cones. Mostly the scoria tends towards the finer end of the size scale and is predominantly of ash (less than a sixteenth of a millimetre in size), coarse ash (one sixteenth to 2 mm in size) or lapilli (2 to 64 mm) grade. Blocks, bombs and accretion balls, which are much larger fragments of lava, can occasionally be seen strewn down the flanks of the cones. The angle of rest of this material on the flanks is usually about 30 degrees.

The scoria cones are mainly a consequence of phreatomagmatic or hydromagmatic explosive activity (the two terms are sometimes used interchangeably) in which ascending magma comes into contact with circulating water. The very liquid magmatic materials, with a relatively low gas content, are thrown into the air and come to rest on the flanks of the vent. As such they can be referred to as Strombolian in type, named after the volcano Stromboli in the Italian Aeolian Islands. The deposits are also known as pyroclastic-fall deposits (or tephra). Wedges of coarse ash and lapilli, very cindery in appearance with angular vesiculated fragments (caused by gas bubbles), are commonplace, more especially near to the core of the vents. Although the ashes and lapilli usually show a very even bedding, varying from a few millimetres to a metre or so in thickness, there are occasions when a distinct, though mild, cross-bedding can be seen, as at El Golfo (Figures 13 & 22). In the case of El Golfo this is due to wave and current activity in shallow seas. Also at El Golfo, and at Pico del Cuchillo (Locality 13), certain massive layers appear to have been laid down by hot materials moving down the flanks of the cones, hence the name ash-flow.

Perhaps the most startling aspect of the volcanic edifices of the island, and generally affecting the scoria cones, is a marked reddening (Rear Cover, Lower). This reddening takes place on all scales, the surface of some cones appearing completely reddened, others just partially reddened. All shades of red can be seen at one place or another and this commonly creates a magnificent panorama of colour when intermingled with the normal black-grey, occasionally white (calichified), tones of most of the cones. The contact between the reds and blacks is sometimes so sharp and cross-cutting as to take on the misleading appearance of an unconformity within the volcanic sequence. On other occasions the contact is more gradational over several metres. There is little doubt that the reddening is caused predominantly by the hydrothermal activities of water, which seem to have taken place late in the history of any given cone. The water, heated by the ascending magma, in which gases such as carbon dioxide, methane, hydrogen and helium were dissolved, may well have partly originated via underground percolation from the adjacent seas, especially during rises in sea-level. The net result is that the permeable deposits are mineralogically altered, particularly the ferro-magnesian minerals, which are partly oxidised into a range of red iron oxides and hydroxides these, in turn, being re-distributed through the deposits. Rainfall might have played some part in the latter.

It is an interesting feature of Lanzarote that the gases emitted during relatively recent volcanic episodes do not seem to have been rich in hydrogen sulphide, sulphur dioxide and other sulphurous material. This is in contrast to the peak of Mount Teide in Tenerife, so that solfataras (sulphur emissions) are absent at present in Lanzarote. However, there might have been a certain amount of sulphurous activity during earlier eruptions, most of the evidence having been destroyed or covered by later volcanic episodes.

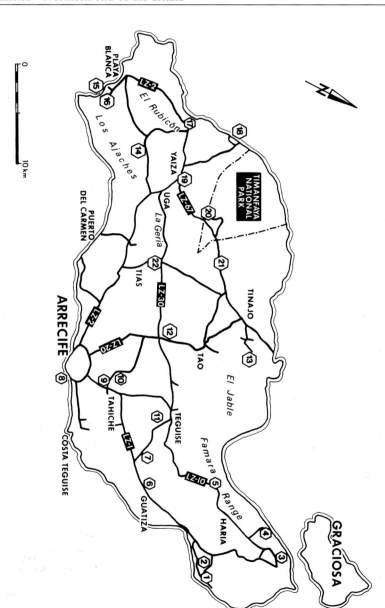

Figure 3. Locality map with road connections

LOCALITIES

As exposures of solid rock are so numerous in Lanzarote it is an invidious task selecting specific localities to be visited.   Nonetheless, there are some that are outstanding for one reason or another and must be seen if a balanced view of the geological history of the island is to be obtained.   For the rest, well they reflect the purely personal preferences of the author.   The localities are loosely grouped into those at the northern end of the island, those in the centre and those at the southwestern end (Figure 3).   They are ordered in the rough form of itineraries but, in reality, they can be easily re-ordered to suit the whim of the visitor.   It is doubtful if all the localities in any given itinerary could be, or indeed should be, fitted into one day.   Take your time absorbing the scenery *en-route* and stop at places of cultural and horticultural interest, such as the ancient capital of the island, Teguise, and the Cactus Garden at Guatiza.   A car is essential and the roads, though narrow in some places, are good apart from certain tracts of the La Geria route.   All the localities are within easy walking distance from the roads.

Northern end of the Island

1.   *Jameos del Agua*

This prime site, reached via the LZ-1 road from Tahiche, then forking right at Arrieta,

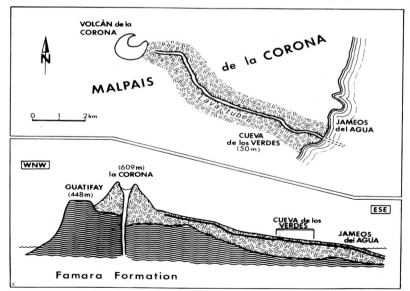

Figure 4. Sketch map of the volcanic tube del Volcán de la Corona.
(After Araña, 1994)

is situated in the midst of a blocky basaltic lava field (Malpais de la Corona) carrying little vegetation apart from varieties of *Euphorbia*, lichens and occasional cacti. It is rewarding geologically for at least two things. Firstly, it gives access for a small entrance fee between the hours of 9.30 a.m. and 6.45 p.m. every day to the seawards end of a major lava tube. In reality this is a complex of interweaving tubes, extending from the foot of the 3000-5000 year old Volcán de la Corona (Crown Volcano) 5 kilometres away to the northwest (Figure 4). Secondly, its surface buildings constitute a Research Centre for Volcanic Studies (Casa de Los Volcánes). The public rooms of the latter are most easily reached via the lava tube (although there are private entrances at the surface) and provide an array of computerised displays and murals describing, among other things, the geological history of the Canary Islands and World volcanicity. Rock specimens characteristic of the islands are also on show, including basaltic blocks with cores of peridotite and dunite derived from the mantle, volcanic bombs and even fossiliferous deposits.

Although the tube has been modified to some extent for commercial reasons as it is, nonetheless, impressive in its height and width, seen more clearly as you descend the entrance steps, via a café and viewing area, towards the permanent lake at the bottom (Cueva de los Lagos). The lake is noted for its colony of blind white crabs, *Munidopsis polymorpha*, a protected species. This is not the termination of the tube, as it is known to extend for some distance eastwards out to sea (El Túnel de la Atlantida). World sea-levels might have been lower at the time it was formed. The full length of the tube is about 8 kilometres. Walking alongside the lake and flank of the tube brings you out again into the open, where the roof either collapsed or was removed. Continue via an attractively laid-out artificial pool until you reach a magnificent concert hall with basaltic walls totally enclosed within the tube, the conception of César Manrique. Steps nearby take you up to the Research Centre displays and refreshments.

2. Cueva de Los Verdes (Green's Cave)

This large hole (jameos) is named after an old farming family of a hundred or so years ago, the Green's. Whereas at Jameos del Agua you just gain a general view of a lava tube, this locality, just to the northwest, shows you in some detail exactly what such a tube complex comprises. The opening hours every day are from 10.00 a.m. to 6.00 p.m., and a small entrance fee is charged. The guide-led, hour-long tours leave at regular intervals and take you westwards up-slope for about 1 kilometre. There is ample time to inspect the nature of the rocks and the structures they exhibit. **However, the collection of material, as at the previous locality, is not allowed under any circumstances.**

There are various things to look for, apart from the general nature and complex structure of the tube, or tubes as there are two superimposed at this point. Near to the entrance (Figure 5, Upper), which leads you into the lower of the tubes, there are sparkling crystalline white patches permeating the basaltic lava. These are said to be carbonates and phosphates precipitated from circulating ground water. Iron oxide staining is widespread in the roof probably caused by chemical reactions b lava and hot gases.

Further along, some upper side sections of the tube walls carry abundant 'lava stalactites', or stafilites (estafilitos) according to the guides, looking almost like roosting bats. They indicate that at certain times the molten lava was confined to the lower part of the tube and the intense heat generated was sufficient to partly melt the walls of the upper part. The splashing of the lava onto the upper walls also probably contributed (Figure 5, Lower). The scouring capability of the mobile lava also

Figure 5. Upper. Entrance to the Cueva de Los Verdes.

Figure 5. Lower. Stafilites ('Lava Stalactites")

brought about a marked horizontal grooving of the walls in places. Along these parts of the traverse the bottom of the tube is as much as, and sometimes exceeds, 50 metres below present ground-level.

The outward termination of the traverse, after walking along a well-defined route, is nothing but spectacular, emphasised by cunningly devised lighting effects. You then ascend into the upper tube of the pair, where it opens-up vertically and laterally, and is partly flooded creating a dramatic Wagnerian underground landscape. The return to the entrance is via a series of slightly un-nerving pathways.

3 Mirador del Río and El Risco

Return to the LZ-1 road and fork right at Yé. The main lead-in road to this marvellous viewpoint (mirador) from Yé runs very close to the top end of deep steep-sided valleys (barrancos) carved into the Mio-Pliocene lavas constituting this

Figure 6. Cliffs at Mirador del Río, looking northwards.

northern end of the Famara massif.   These are just two of the many found at the northern and southern ends of the island and probably were initiated during late Miocene to early Pliocene times during phases when sea-levels were much lower than at present.   The bottom of the second barranco is wide and relatively flat and fertile, which leads one to believe that the bottom partly comprises soil washed down (and no doubt humanly transported sometimes) from near to the level of the road. As you get closer to the entrance to the Mirador del Río you will see that there are extensive exposures on both sides of the road of red-brown soil profiles, anything up to 10 metres thick.   The profiles incorporate hard layers up to 40 centimetres thick, some of which show typical crusts of caliche.

Despite being a focus for the tourism trade, parking at the mirador, created by César Manrique, is not difficult.   A small fee gains entrance between the hours of 10.00 a.m. and 5.45 p.m. every day.   The basaltic lavas forming the upper part of the 450 metre high cliffs (El Risco), which are on view from the restaurant and viewing platforms, are of Upper Miocene age, thinly capped in places by Pliocene.   Note the slaggy, ashy tops of successive lava flows, which have weathered out to give a mildly stepped profile (Figure 6).   Columnar jointing is especially evident in two lavas towards the top of the cliff, to the right of the platforms.   There are extensive scree fans at the base of the cliffs which grade into a narrow, flat coastal strip, where you can pick out the site of an old disused salina (Salinas del Río).

The northeast - southwest aligned black and orange-red tephra Pleistocene cones of Graciosa island stand out well from the mirador and the nearest one, Montana del Mojón (185 m), at its southern end provides a textbook example of strata V-ing downdip.   The island is accessible by boat from Orzola (25 minutes).

All the time spent at the mirador and along the lead-in roads you cannot but be aware of the looming presence of the breached Holocene Volcán de la Corona to the south, classical in form (Rear Cover, Upper).

There is a tremendous panorama looking further southwards, into the far distance, encompassing the low-lying El Jable with a string of aligned Pleistocene minor cones, such as Juan del Hierro (199 m) and the larger Soo (293 m).   Beyond those is the full range of volcanoes of the Timanfaya National Park.

Now take the minor narrow road running southwest from the mirador along the crest of the Famara cliffs (El Risco).   The views are again stunning.   About 2 kilometres further on, where the road turns inland and where there is a width and height restriction notice for vehicles, there is a block-paved track leading off to the west with a small car park.   Around you is a blocky, black cindery lava, almost forming a dyke-like wall in places, and this is a tongue of the Holocene Corona eruptions, which flowed westwards along a depression in the Miocene Famara Formation lavas, between Guatifay (448 m) to the south and the cliffs to the north.   Follow the cobbled path and lava flow to the edge of the cliffs, where there is yet another superbly sited mirador.   Looking north from it is the stepped profile of El Risco. The view to the south is even more exciting as, some 50-70 metres distant, you can

Figure 7. Corona Group lavas cascading down the Famara cliffs.

see where the Corona lava has flowed over the edge of the cliff. The tongues of lava dip steeply down the cliff face at about 60 degrees (Figure 7).

4. Mirador de Guinate

From the El Risco mirador return to the main LZ-10 road leading towards Haría. *En-route* notice further exposures of red-brown soils with caliche layers up to 2 metres in thickness. Turn off westwards along a broad, relatively fertile valley to Guinate. Pass by the scattered farm buildings and houses, and the Tropical or Parrot Park, until you reach the end of the road and the mirador. There is ample parking. Immediately to the north is a magnificent cliff section exposing columnar-jointed lavas in the Miocene Famara Formation (Figure 8). You can pick out at least four lava flows that show this cooling structure, the topmost one being the most impressive. The tops of the flows carry red profiles caused by contemporaneous weathering, some more than a metre in thickness. A particularly good example of this rubefaction occurs just above eye-level when standing at the end of the road. A short distance to the south there is a spectacular sharp-edged cliff backed by another flat-bottomed barranco.

*Figure 8. Columnar jointing and rubefaction horizon (R) in
the Famara Formation at Guinate.*

5. Restaurante los Helechos

This is an excellent viewpoint on the LZ-10, where refreshments can be obtained,
and is about 1 kilometre south of the Mirador del Haría, where parking is very
restricted.   The view from the Restaurante is again quite spectacular.   Looking to
the north, towards Haría and beyond, you are, in effect, looking along a
topographically pronounced part of the eastern flank of the Famara massif.   The
much younger Holocene Volcán de la Corona stands out well in the distance.   The
lower slopes in the middle distance are comparatively well-vegetated.   Here and
there the typically red-brown soils derived from the weathering of the old massif
stand out.   Where the slopes have not been terraced these soils are being actively
eroded into small-scale barrancos.   From the viewing area and extending eastwards
towards the coast near to Arrieta is the major and very deep Barranco de Chafaris.

Localities - Northern end of the Island

The lower levels of this Barranco are carved in the oldest Miocene exposed lavas of the Famara massif, the outcrop of which has widened considerably compared with just a few kilometres to the north.

6. Guatiza

Most of the main road (LZ-1) leading from Tahiche to Guatiza and the Cactus Garden passes over Pleistocene volcanics mantled by scrubby, infertile brown soils partly incised by minor barrancos. The soils appear to have flattened out the usual irregular topography of the lavas, creating relatively smooth surfaces. About 2 kilometres south of Guatiza the road passes between the La Caldera (324 m) on the east and the Montaña de Guenia (358 m) on the west, these being Upper - Middle Pleistocene in age. There has been a certain amount of working of the lapilli and ash deposits on the flanks of La Caldera that face the road. The material is used as a kind mulch for vines, as a top dressing for cultivated prickly pears (host plant for a Mexican insect - *Dactylopius coccus*, source of the natural crimson dye cochineal) and for ornamental purposes. Prickly pears are commonplace in the fields adjacent to the LZ-1 between Guatiza and Mala.

An intriguing aspect of the workings at La Caldera is the way in which the worked vertical faces, dipping at about 30° or so, remain in place. This is a reflection of the relatively high degree of frictional resistance of the constituent angular particles and relatively high shear strength of the deposits in an essentially dry environment (Figure 10).

A few hundred metres to the south of the entrance to Guatiza note how the ground flattens out and is occupied by fertile brown soils (loams). These are derived from

Figure 9. Reworked soil pits just to the south of Guatiza

the old weathered Famara massif to the west and probably transporte
of major barrancos, seen to the west, which cut the massif and merge into the flat
alluvial tract.

It is possible to inspect closely these soils in an extensive series of roadside workings
(Figure 9). Cars can be parked just off the main road in an area overlooking the pits.
About 6-7 metres of loam are exposed carrying thin lenses and seams, up to 50 cm,
of rounded and sub-rounded pebbles of basalt and caliche. The deposits are
stratified, but non-laminated, and carry a sprinkling of terrestrial snail shells.

3. El Mojón

This locality straddles a gently descending road leading from Teseguite (and Teguise)
towards the main LZ-1 Tahiche - Guatiza road. It is situated about 2 km east-
southeast of El Mojón and comprises an extensive series of shallow pits in coarse ash
and lapilli on the fertile southern flanks (Vega Vieja) of the Upper - Middle
Pleistocene Montaña de Guenia (358 m). One of the objects of interest is not so
much the ash fall, of which about 7 m is exposed in various faces, but the capping of
caliche. This capping generally has thicknesses reaching 60 cm, but can reach as
much as 1.5 m in vertical pedestals left by the workmen. The more friable lower
parts of the pedestals have been much affected by strong winds, thus becoming very
photogenic (Figure 10).

However, there is much more to this locality than meets the immediate eye. By
walking northwards for a short distance, towards the volcanic peak, you will first
come across a classically shaped, though relatively small, barranco - the upper length

*Figure 10. Caliche-capped pedestals of ash and lapilli, near El Mojón. In the background
are the ash workings on the flank of La Caldera (see Locality 6)*

Figure 11. The top of the 5 metre thick caliche profile (C) capped by a soil (S) and bands of lava and ash.

of the Barranco Espoleta. It is possible to cross the barranco by a clear trackway. Once across you will see a 5 metre thick caliche layer capped by 1 metre of brown soil (Figure 11). This caliche and soil development clearly represents a long period of weathering and suggests that the underlying parent volcanics are probably of Lower Pleistocene age. Overlying the soil are alternate bands of lava and black ash, some partly calichified, belonging to the outpourings of the younger Montaña de Guenia. At some stage the ashes extended across the line of the present barranco as far as the roadside pits and beyond. Thus the barranco either post-dates the late Pleistocene volcanic eruption or has been re-incised along its earlier course.

Central Area

8. Castillo de San José & Playa de la Arena

These prime localities are situated near to the eastern end of the Arrecife northern by-pass (circunvalación) and the Castillo, the latter being associated with Manrique-based activities in 1988, includes a museum of contemporary art. The castle, open

Figure 12. Upper. Seawards termination of the lava tongue of the 1730-1736 eruptions.

Figure 12. Lower. Typical ropy surface of the lava flow at Playa de la Arena

from 11.00 a.m. to 9 p.m. every day, has ample parking space and is built on a 30 metre high promontory composed of lenticular grey basalts of Upper - Middle Pleistocene age. At the foot of the cliff beneath the splendidly designed restaurant can be seen in plan good polygonal jointing on various scales, a surface expression of columnar joints and irregular cooling.

You can either walk or drive northeastwards and upslope along the main road for about 400 metres until you come to a flat roadside area, suitable for parking. This overlooks a narrow bay with a sandy beach, Playa de la Arena. The view from the top eastwards encompasses a distinctive low-lying outcrop of blocky, very black lava in the centre of the bay and extending into the sea (Figure 12, Upper). Inland, and through an eyesore of a scruffy dump, there is a northern extension of the basalt lava, marked by ridge-like outcrops. This lava is the seaward end of the same tongue to be seen at the Manrique Foundation (Locality 9) and is part of the 1730-1736 volcanic episode. It appears to have flowed down a shallow topographic depression into the sea.

Descend to the beach via the steps to inspect the lava more closely passing *en-route* more of the Upper-Middle Pleistocene lavas, some as much as 6 metres thick. The 1730-1736 lava is vesicular, but the most interesting feature is excellent ropy surfaces to some of the blocks and very photogenic (Figure 12, Lower). You can also pick out the remains of a partly collapsed lava tube measuring about 6 metres across and traceable for about 30 metres. Along the edge of the collapsed section it is also possible to see, despite a degree of weathering, 'lava stalactites' (stafilites) originally formed in the upper wall and roof zone of the tube.

9. *Fundación César Manrique*

Situated at Taro de Tahiche, just off the LZ-3 road, this former home of Manrique is now the headquarters of the Foundation. It consists of a series of stylish buildings built on the eastern edge of a tongue of basaltic lava flow associated with the eruptions of Timanfaya over the period 1730-1736. The narrow tongue abuts the flank of Montaña Maneje to the west and extends southwards to the coast at Playa de la Arena.

The buildings partly occupy what are referred to as natural 'gas bubbles', which were generated in the lava during its cooling stages, but whether the 'bubbles' were part of a collapsed volcanic tube or a lava channel is a moot point. Another interesting feature, visible through the large plate-glass windows at ground level, is the development of ropy 'custard-skin' surfaces to the lava, a function of the viscosity of the material at the time.

10. *Montaña de Maneje*

About 1.5 kilometres to the west of the Foundation, along the road leading to San Bartolomé, and adjacent to what seems to be horticultural research buildings and

Figure 13. Typical fine bedding in ash-fall deposits on the flanks of a volcano

grounds, is a previously worked pit on the southern flank of the volcano (291 m), which is of Middle to Upper Pleistocene age. Having parked your vehicle at the roadside on the western side of the horticultural establishment, it is necessary to walk northwards up a gently sloping, well-worn track for about 200 metres to the narrow entrance to the pit. The walls of the entrance comprise a good example of thinly bedded and laminated basaltic coarse ash and lapilli, very friable to the touch. The individual layers generally sustain an even thickness, though here and there, there are structures that resemble isolated ripples, probably moulded during turbulence (Figure 13). The sharp bases and tops of the layers indicate pauses between each fall, maybe lasting only a few minutes during the height of the activity. The sorting within any given layer is not particularly good, with larger lapilli irregularly scattered in what is essentially a coarse ash. What emphasises the layering is the colouring, mainly blue-black, but with an interleaving of creamy layers reflecting slight differences in composition and texture. In the pit proper the layering becomes very pronounced towards the top of the face, possibly because there has been an infiltration into some of the more permeable layers of calcium carbonate, making them a little more resistant to weathering. This seems to be borne out by the presence of a caliche layer, up to a metre in thickness, immediately above.

11. Montaña Guanapay

The prominent volcanic crater of Guanapay (452 m), perfect in its circular plan, is possibly early Pleistocene in age, though may be older. It is capped on its western rim by a castle known as Castillo Santa Barbara or Castillo de Guanapay. This is easily reached by a side road, off the main LZ-10 road through Teguise, the attractive old capital of Lanzarote. Teguise was established as a town in the 15th century and is well-worth exploring. The Castillo, which has limited parking space, was built towards the end of the 14th century and now houses a museum. From the rim of the crater there are extensive views to the north towards the edge of the Famara cliffs and west across the low-lying Pleistocene lava fields of El Jable to Pico Colorado (203 m), above Soo village. The view southwestwards takes in most of the Timanfaya range. There are no distant views eastwards.

12. Tao

These pits are located on the western side of the main road (LZ-20) leading from the Monumento Al Campesino to Tao village and are about 1 kilometre south of the village. The 15 metre tall Monumento, another Manrique creation erected in 1968

Figure 14. Near-vertical faces in ash pits, south of Tao village

to praise the farm workers of Lanzarote, is complemented by an adjacent first class restaurant, a snack bar open between 12.30 and 4.00 p.m., with all the usual facilities, and a farmhouse museum and shop.

The pits are on the eastern side of a small Middle to Upper Pleistocene volcanic ash cone known as Lomo de Camacho (374 m), to the immediate southeast of Montaña Tamia (550 m) (sometimes named as Tao on tourist road maps). The innermost working faces are some 10-14 metres high and, though formed of the usual basaltic friable materials, stand vertically, a tribute to the interlocking nature of the loose particles and, no doubt, to the protective influence of a well-developed rubbly caliche capping (Figure 14). The capping here has weathered to an iron-rich deep orange-brown colour in contrast to some caliche profiles on the island which remain creamy white (see Locality 7).

There is another volcanic cone worth pointing out, just one and a half kilometres to the north of Tao village *en-route* to Tiagua and just to the east of the LZ-20. This is the Montaña del Clerido Duarte, relatively small (301 m) but associated with the last major eruptive episode in the island. Over the period 31st July to 24th October 1824 a breach some 13 kilometres long, and aligned east-northeast - west-southwest, opened up extending from the vicinity of the Montañas del Fuego/ El Diablo restaurant and centre area in the Timanfaya National Park. Clerido Duarte marks the eastern extremity of the breach.

13. Pico del Cuchillo

This none-too-prominent semi-circular feature (181 m), usually referred to as a caldera, is situated adjacent to the outskirts of the village of El Cuchillo. It is reached by taking a minor road northeastwards just to the north of Tinajo. Take care in El Cuchillo village to turn right (east), otherwise you will find yourself back on the La Santa road. Travel for about one kilometre until you see a white driveway to the left and a small concrete building located on the crest of a northwest-facing slope. Park your vehicle, then walk across rough ground eastwards for about 100 metres, where you will find yourself on the western rim of the caldera (Figure 15). The view is splendid, with the ash layers well exposed in the wall of the crater to your right and yellow windblown Quaternary sands straight-ahead, piled up against the distant low northern wall. The floor of the caldera, once the site of lagoons, is flat, fertile and used for horticultural purposes. Soo village and the Pleistocene Pico Colorado (203 m) can be seen in the middle distance and, on a clear day, the vast precipitous wall of the Famara cliffs.

The degraded caldera is probably early Pleistocene in age and is breached towards the north. It is totally surrounded by Middle to Upper Pleistocene basaltic lavas, which flowed mainly southwards and are variably dated as 700,000 and 30,000 years old. The lavas swept around and penetrated the breached side, partly blocking it and helping to create conditions in the bottom of the caldera suitable for the formation of small lagoons. Sediments accumulated in these lagoons on at least two occasions.

Figure 15. View looking northeastwards from the western rim of the caldera with Pico del Cuchillo, formed of well bedded ashes, to the right and lighter coloured Quaternary windblown sands to the left piled against the lower northeastern rim.

Like a few of the other volcanoes in Lanzarote, such as El Golfo (Locality 18), the eruption in early Pleistocene times appears to have been located very near to the coast or in shallow coastal waters - it is now 2 kilometres away from the sea.

The surviving southern and eastern walls of the caldera comprise layers of lapilli and coarse ash, some massively or uniformly bedded, other more finely banded and laminated as seen elsewhere. Some of the massive massively bedded layers are probably surge or ash-flow deposits. Two main episodes of activity are recognised, though the first was the most prolonged. Sharp breaks occur in both ash sequences, indicative of pauses in deposition. Blocks of lava, up to 2 cubic metres in size, occur especially towards the base of the sequences. Bombs up to 50 centimetres are distributed throughout, some containing enclaves or cores of gabbro or dunite, both derived from close to the Earth's mantle.

Localities - Central Area

Possibly the most intriguing aspect is the presence in the ashes of a relatively large number of well rounded pebbles of coarse, shelly limestone, as much as 40 centimetres in size, though usually between 10-20 centimetres. They carry microfossils identified as being of Palaeocene, possibly Cretaceous, age. These limestones appear to have been laid down originally in shallow littoral seas, then were subject to erosion by uplift above sea-level before being incorporated into the ascending basaltic magma during Pleistocene times. Quite a complicated story! If you want to inspect the strata in the caldera walls at the foot of the Pico the best approach is from the main road at the western end, but it is quite a trek.

Southwestern Area

14. Femés (Los Ajaches)

Whichever way one approaches Femés, whether from the east via the LZ-2 and LZ-702 roads from Arrecife and Yaiza or from the west via Las Breñas and Playa Blanca, the Ajaches range is very impressive. Consisting as it does of some of the oldest (Middle Miocene) volcanics of Lanzarote, a large proportion of which are basaltic lavas and weather-out in a step-like fashion, the range dominates its immediate low-lying surroundings. From the eastern side the road winds steeply upwards from near Uga, passing on the immediate west the lower scoriaceous slopes of Caldera Riscarda (446 m), a Pleistocene volcano. The ground on the eastern side of the road falls away quite steeply with a marked barranco leading eastern and flattening out towards low ground. Two sets of scoria deposits outcrop on its flanks with a clear angular discordance between them. One set belongs to the Caldera Riscarda and the other set belongs to a subsidiary cone of Pico Naos (415 m) to the south.

After passing through Las Casitas de Femés the tarmac road continues southwestwards along a broad, flat, relatively fertile valley cutting through the heart of the Ajaches range. The flat nature reflects the partial infilling of the valley bottom by soils and other weathered debris generated on the surrounding slopes, then transported over the millennia into the bottom. There are pits adjacent to the road where the loamy soils have been worked for horticultural purposes. Note the well-rounded, mature-looking topography, well-vegetated, with heads of barrancos carved into the steeper slopes bounding the main depression. Femés village, with its attractive church and eating place, is a splendid vantage-point on the western fringe of the Ajaches. The view westwards from the Balcón de Femés encompasses lava fields of Middle to Upper Pleistocene age, forming the El Rubicon plain area on which Las Breñas is built, and Lower Pleistocene lavas on which Playa Blanca is built. Playa Blanca, a pleasant coastal resort, and Montaña Roja (194 m) can be seen in the far west. In the very far distance on a clear day the tip of the island of Fuerteventura, another member of the Canaries volcanic archipelago with numerous volcanic peaks, can also be picked out. Fuerteventura can be reached by the regular car ferries from Playa Blanca (40 minutes).

The steep descent by road from Femés is down a prominent steep-sided barranco cut in the Middle Miocene volcanics carrying a few northeast - southwest trending dykes. There then comes into view the impressive westwards-facing escarpment of the Ajaches range, which reaches a height of 560 metres at Hacha Grande (Figure 16). The face is dissected by barrancos and gullies, most of which merge into extensive fans of scree that are lighter coloured at their fresher apex end. The regular layering of the volcanics stands out well on the face and, even at a distance, it is possible to see columnar jointing in some of the thicker lava flows.

Continuing along the Femés - Las Breñas road and past a junction with a dirt road only suitable for 4-wheel drive vehicles, leading southwards to Playa Blanca, brings

Figure 16. View looking south near Femés of the Ajaches range, with Pico Redondo to the left and Hacha Grande to the right.

you to some extensive and spectacular roadside quarries in coarse ash and lapilli (Rear Cover, lower). The deposits were laid down on the southern flanks of Caldera de Masión (352 m), probably of Middle to Upper Pleistocene age, which abuts Atalaya de Femés (608 m). Here you have an excellent example of late-stage hydrothermal alteration that characterises so many of the younger cones of the island. It is instructive to work your way progressively along the foot of the worked faces, which are more than 30 metres high in places. At the main (eastern) entrance you are confronted with typical bedded and laminated pyroclastic fall deposits showing marked reddening. Some very coarse layers and lenses are up to 2 metres in thickness and include a high proportion of small bombs, up to 30 centimetres across set in an ash matrix. About 100 or so metres further along on the right (east) it will become apparent that the colour of the pyroclastics is changing to a distinct blue-black. The change is relatively sharp in so far that it occurs over a distance of a few metres, the deposits in the gradational zone being predominantly grey. This zone cuts obliquely across the primary stratification, so there is no doubt that the reddening is a secondary alteration effect. While at this eastern end of the workings note that a 75 centimetre caliche layer is still preserved in places. This probably mantled most of the surface of the volcano, but had to be removed prior to extracting the ashes.

15. Punta del Aguila (Castillo de las Coloradas)

This locality is situated about 2.5 kilometres east of Playa Blanca and can be reached either on foot as a pleasant, though rough in places, coastal walk from the eastern promenade of Playa Blanca or by car, travelling eastwards along the tarmac road towards Playa de las Coloradas. Turn right after the first roundabout, then first left followed by first right. The stubby cylindrical Castillo, looking like a Martello Tower, is in sight all the time and there is no problem in parking hear to it. However, there is much construction work taking place in the vicinity.

The basaltic lavas that constitute the steep 15-20 metre high cliffs, and extend for more than half a kilometre on each side of the point, are mapped as belonging to the Ajaches Middle Miocene sequence (Figure 17). A mild degree of columnar jointing towards the base of the flows can just be picked out from the cliff top and there are polygonally shaped fallen blocks scattered on the shore face. The lavas vary considerably in thickness when traced along the cliff faces and this can be observed without the necessity of descending to beach level. However, if you want to look a little more closely, it is possible to descend at the far end of the promontory on which the castle stands, exerting great care as underfoot can be quite slippery. The going is equally rough and boulder strewn, and requires attention to the state of the tide, once you are at beach level.

Figure 17. Middle Miocene lavas, showing columnar jointing, and dykes, the one in the centre being multiple. A thick lenticular zone of reddening (rubefaction) (R) occurs just below the uppermost lava.

A feature of the tops of the lavas is a reddening (rubefaction) caused by subaerial weathering either during pauses in volcanic activity or caused by the active lava streams being diverted elsewhere for a lengthy period. The lenticular zones of weathering, as exhibited particularly well on the western and eastern sides of the castle cliffs, can be several metres thick.

The other striking feature of the cliffs is a complex of steeply dipping basaltic feeder dykes, mostly single intrusions but occasionally multiple, and mostly post-dating the original weathering of the tops of the associated lavas. There seems to be at least two generations of dyke intrusion in this area, weathered brown varieties being interspersed with fresher-looking grey varieties.

Before leaving this locality note the bevelling at the top of the cliffs both here and to the east and southeast towards Punta del Papagayo, a feature also observable from Salinas del Janubio (Locality 17). This bevelling appears to be a marine planation formed when sea-level was higher, possibly in mid-Pleistocene times (see p. 10).

16. las Coloradas

A short, well-defined path along the cliff top eastwards from the Castillo soon joins a well-paved promenade, with ornamental gardens, and where further dykes can be readily seen. The promenade leads down, via a new holiday complex, to a small bay.

Turn inland and walk along the line of a barranco for a few hundred metres until you reach the expanding residential village of las Coloradas. Alternatively, return to the main Playa Blanca road, turn right and continue down into the village. The point to aim for is a large roundabout with five lead-off roads and a dolmen-like edifice in its centre. It is here that further dykes can be seen in a number of roadside exposures cutting through grey-black and reddened ashes and lavas of Middle Miocene age. The blue-black and brown weathered dykes trend northeast - southwest and north - south and are between 45 centimetres and 3 metres in width. Some have clear very fine-grained chilled margins, as much as 7 centimetres wide (Figure 18). Dips vary from 30° to near-vertical. Unfortunately, landscaping by builders in recent years has obscured some fine exposures in thicker multiple dykes but, by searching around, you can still see evidence of such. These present outcrops clearly confirm, on textural and colour grounds, that there were two generations of dyke intrusion. If you continue working your way around the outcrops adjacent to the roundabout and its lead-in roads you will eventually come across dykes cross-cutting each other (Figure 19).

Figure 18. The dyke to the left has a margin which has chilled where it is in contact with the reddened lava (R) to the right. Scale in centimetres

Figure 19. Cross-cutting dykes at las Coloradas.

Figure 20. Upper. View southwards across the salt workings with the mid-Pleistocene raised marine platform in the distance.

Figure 20. Lower. Upper Miocene Tias Formation dykes.

While you are here, if you examine the lavas, and even the dykes, very carefully you will see that some have a distinct flow texture, emphasised by the alignment of the small phenocrysts of white feldspar. These rocks are trachy-basalts.

In travelling back from las Colorados and Playa Blanca to Salinas de Janubio along the LZ-2, note that at about 4 kilometres along the way there is a cliff-like feature. This marks the southwestern edge of Middle to Upper Pleistocene lava flows of the El Rubicon area resting on Lower Pleistocene lavas. The feature resembles an old cliff-line and, if so, might have a genetic connection with the marine platform observed from Punta del Aguila (Locality 15) and also to be seen from Locality 17. The village of Las Breñas is perched on the edge of what appears to be another series of Pleistocene lavas.

17. Salinas de Janubio

The side road leading northwestwards off the main arterial Playa Blanca -Yaiza road (LZ-2) soon brings you to viewpoints overlooking what is the last remaining active salt works in Lanzarote. Sea-water is pumped up from the natural lagoon to a slightly higher level basin then, when the salinity has risen to about 25 per cent, the brine is fed into the artificial evaporation pans. When the salts have crystallised out they are then scraped up for final drying.

The smooth marine-bevelled basaltic cliffs to the south are predominantly Lower Pleistocene in age. However, the rocks on which the salt works are founded have been mapped as a scooped-out depression (probably the site of an ancient barranco system) on an inlier of the Upper Miocene Tias succession (Figure 20, Upper).

Turn off the road overlooking the salinas and follow a metalled track down to the pans, parking at the foot of the slope near to a research building. The building is located at the mouth of a small east-west trending barranco. The exposures on the northern side of the building comprise lava lenses, up to 1.5 metres thick, and ashes cut through by three prominent dykes, 80 cm, 4 m and 30 cm in width, all trending north-northeast - south-southwest. The widest dyke, which can also be traced on the southern side of the barranco, appears to be multiple in type. The exposure is shot through with calcite veins (Figure 20, Lower).

On leaving the Salinas note that the beach is formed of black volcanic pebbles and sand.

18. El Golfo

The coast road from the salt works to El Golfo crosses over the impressive black-hued lava field associated with the major episode of volcanic activity between 1730 and 1736. The road is very scenic. At Los Hervideros (the 'boiling springs') there

Figure 21. Columnar jointing in the 1730-1736 lavas at Hervideros.

is ample parking space and walkways laid out over the blocky basaltic lavas from which you can view closely the highly corrugated coastline with its sea-caves, stacks, enlarged fissures and blow-holes.   Columnar jointing is well-developed in places (Figure 21).   By looking inland you are presented with magnificent views into the hinterland of the island.   The Ajaches range stands out prominently to the right (southeast) and directly ahead and to the left you are looking into the volcanic heartland of the Timanfaya National Park.   The distinctive alignment of many of the volcanic peaks is very evident. The sharp rim of the Caldera de Chozas (83 m) can be picked out just in front of Montaña de la Vieja Gabriela (226 m) and, to the left, is Montaña Bermaja (106 m), a dissected scoria cone. All these are of Middle to Upper Pleistocene age and now, being surrounded by the younger 18th century lavas, can be referred to as islotes (small barren islands).

Continuing northwards you eventually reach a road junction with a very sharp right-angled bend. Do not turn right but follow carefully the left fork for a short distance before parking. This is the main access route to a remarkable half-destroyed crater of the Pleistocene volcano known as Montaña del Golfo (152 m), another islote, and the crescent shaped bay or 'golfo'.

At this southern car park the first thing that strikes you is the colour changes in the ashes forming the immediate cliff-face. Close inspection reveals that the grey-brown coloured material is a veneer of variable thickness covering the orange-brown material. The implication is that there has been some significant alteration processes affecting the original ash. If you now examine the orange-brown ash at the northern end of the car park, adjacent to a concrete hut, you will find that the deposits show cross-bedding, minor channelling and contain rounded to sub-angular pebbles of porphyritic basalt (Figure 22). Occasionally basalt boulders (bombs) dropped into the ash cause distortion of the bedding. All the evidence points to El Golfo being a volcano erupting into shallow, current-swept seas. It originated via hydromagmatic processes and the orange-brown colour probably relates to reactions between the basic ash and sea-water. One of the products of these changes is palagonite, a complex mineral-like substance, and it is this that has been identified in the ashes and accounts for their bright colour.

Proceeding further down the entrance track-way, note the small-scale faulting along northeast-southwest lines caused by gravitational settling of the material during explosive phases. You can also observe honeycomb weathering, the relative hardness almost vitreous nature of the palagonite ashes, and the variable degree of stratification in the deposits. Some sections seem devoid of any form of bedding or lamination, which suggests ash-flow deposition whereas others are well-bedded and laminated, indicative of ash-fall. This variability is especially noticeable in the large sea-stack emerging from the beach. (Also see Locality 13).

On reaching the beach, the impressive and very complex-looking face of El Golfo, with its razor-sharp, scalloped edges, meets the eye (Figure 23). Again the colour variations are very marked due to slippage and erosion of the grey-brown weathered veneer to the palagonite ashes. At the northern end occurs a thin capping of well-bedded blue-black ashes and lapilli, dipping at about 30 degrees to the west. There are many slipped blocks. There is also a significant degree of hydrothermal alteration and reddening of these later ash deposits.

Figure 22. Cross-bedding and fine bedding in palagonitic ash and lapilli, with occasional bombs (lower centre).

At the base of the cliff is a permanent lagoon (Laguna de los Clicos) separated from the open sea by a wide bar or barrier (tombolo), which extends from headland to headland and is composed of reworked black volcanic sand, pebbles and a sprinkling of caliche slabs. The lagoon is fed from the sea by percolation through the permeable beach deposits and, in most lights, has a green colour predominantly due to the presence of algae.

Figure 23. The main face of El Golfo with the lagoon.

Return to the parking area and continue along the road leading to the northern side of El Golfo, where you will find ample parking space opposite a café. Take the rising path to the south, well-worn by coach parties, which takes you to an excellent viewing platform for examining the main cliff face again. There are some interesting exposures at the path side in the brown, black and grey ash layers, including some small-scale cross-bedding and very curious-looking columns or pedestals, up to 1.5 metres tall, which are the upstanding remains of caliche pipes and veins. The softer, more friable ashes have been weathered and eroded away leaving the harder, more cohesive caliche standing.

19. Yaiza

Travelling southeastwards from El Golfo to Yaiza takes you across the extensive lava field generated during 1730-1736, passing by the Pleistocene islote of Montaña de la Vieja Gabriela (226 m). Note the marked colour banding within the ashes of the volcano and the splendid, fresh-looking scree fans at the base (Figure 24). From the roundabout west of Yaiza the by-pass takes you across the southern edge of one of the lava fronts which, in 1731, looked as though it would overwhelm the attractive village (founded on late Pleistocene and Middle Miocene volcanics) (Front Cover).

20. Timanfaya (Montañas del Fuego)

This National Park, created in 1974 and covering an area of 51 square kilometres, encompasses the crowning geologic and scenic glory of Lanzarote. The temptation

Figure 24. The scree fans of Montaña de la Vieja Gabriela.

is to visit it early on in a geological tour of the island, but this should be resisted until you have become familiar with and laid your hands on the various rock types and volcanic structures in other areas. The point being that you cannot stroll wherever you will in the Park and it is illegal to stop except at defined parking places and it is certainly **illegal to collect specimens.**

Only designated coaches are allowed on the Ruta de Los Volcánes in the summit area and, although they pause at certain points, it is only rarely that you are permitted to descend from the coach, and then only for a few minutes for photographic purposes.

The entry into the Park is probably most rewarding from the Yaiza end via the ascending straight road LZ-67, leading towards the summit area. In doing so you gain some idea of the extent of the basaltic lava field (malpais) created between the 1st September 1730 and the 16th April 1736. The lichen-mantled lavas are mainly of the blocky type. Drive past the camel trail, noting 200 metres further on a collapsed lava-tube or lava channel on the right-hand side of the road. You then pass a partly breached caldera once occupied by a lava lake, before descending to the entrance to the 'Mountains of Fire'. Access is between the hours of 9.00 a.m. and 5.45 p.m. every day. Having paid the appropriate fee at the entrance, the lead-in road takes you up to the Manrique-designed El Diablo restaurant area adjacent to the Pico del Fuego o Timanfaya (510 m) and the Islote de Hilario (472 m).

Figure 25. Upper. Small vent adjacent to El Diablo restaurant.

Figure 25. Lower. View from the car park towards the northwest showing a number of steep-sided hornitos

Figure 26. Upper. Hydrothermally altered tephra (H) in a roadside vent, near Montaña Rajada.

Figure 26. Lower. Montaña Rajada seen from across the 1730-1736 lava field.

Coaches run at regular intervals during daylight hours on the Ruta de Los Volcánes. What you will see is spectacular, but has to be absorbed and recognised quickly. The things to look out for in this complex of islotes of Middle to Upper Pleistocene age flanked and surmounted by the Holocene volcanics, include a selection of volcanic cones and vents of many sizes of which over a hundred are recognised (Figure 25). The east-northeast - west-southwest alignment of cones along deep-seated fracture lines is clear in places. A few of the cones, including ones visible from the car park, are small, very steep-sided and chimney-like composed to a large degree of bombs and blocks of lava. These are known as hornitos. The bulk, however, tend to be classical in shape and formed predominantly of lapilli and coarse ash, with sprinklings of bombs, blocks and accretion balls of lava. The grooved trails made by the latter as they have skidded down the lower ash flanks of some cones are most marked.

The pyroclastic falls are hydrothermally reddened in places (Figure 26, Upper) and some of the finer material appears to have been subsequently mobilised and moulded by strong winds into what closely resemble orange-red desert dunes, with rippled surfaces.

The 1730-1736 blue-black lavas occupying the lower lying ground have flowed around and between most of the older cones. At certain points you can see the lava field extending westwards and northwestwards as far as the sea, 6-7 kilometres away. In less busy periods coaches take you to a viewpoint near to Montaña Rajada ('Split Mountain': 377 m), named after a marked breach in its rim (Figure 26, Lower). A lava channel and partly collapsed volcanic tube, traceable for several hundreds of metres, leads away from the breach. Even if this is missed out, the standard coach route runs down the centre of another channel or tube, where the roof has been excavated.

21. Centro de Visitantes

The Centre, open from 10.00 a.m. until 5.00 p.m. every day, is located about 2.5 kilometres along the LZ-67 road towards Mancha Blanca and Tinajo. Entrance to this spacious modern exhibition building, founded on a 1730-1736 lava train, is free. There are all the usual facilities, including a shop, library and many excellent displays illustrating the geology of Lanzarote, but no restaurant. There is ample parking space. Film shows dealing with the natural history of the island are laid on at regular intervals. You can inspect closely, in the lower levels, a cross-section through a typical olivine-bearing lava flow and the lavas are again well seen from the viewing platform extending from the building. Notice, incidentally, that the geology map on show differs in detail from that in this guide in the Playa Blanca - El Rubicon area.

48

Localities - Southwestern Area

22. La Geria

Take the road southwards from Mancha Blanca, which cuts across the grain of the volcanic terrain, until you meet the main east-west Masdache-Uga road (LZ-30), at this point a rather narrow well-used route carved out along the southern flank of the Timanfaya eruptions. Turn westwards towards Uga and into an area known as La Geria, noted for its vine fields and vineries (bodegas). This relatively fertile ground, and there is a similar tract to the east extending beyond Masdache, has been created by prevailing northeasterly winds blowing fine ash away from the volcanic centres of Timanfaya and draping it over the adjacent lower lying countryside. The ash is now obscured by a mantle of lapilli distributed by the land owners (see below).

About a kilometre along, the road suddenly cuts through the leading west-facing edge of a tongue of the 1730-1736 lava flows resting on a foundation of Middle to Upper Pleistocene volcanics (Figure 27). A close inspection of this olivine-bearing basaltic lava is well worthwhile, so walk along the lava front, which is 6-8 metres high, for a short distance. In places it is possible to see typical cross-sections through individual lobes of the lava, with a solid then vesicular blue-black base passing upwards into flow-breccia and cindery ash. At intervals there are arcuate re-entrants in the face suggestive of collapsed lava tubes or, maybe, lava channels. By scrambling up onto the upper surface of the flows you can deduce the probable line of these tubes from a series of depressions.

Figure 27. Southern edge of the 1730-1736 lava flows, near to Volcán de Peña Paloma, La Geria.

Now continue southwestwards along the main road for a further 600 metres. At the T-junction, with a road on the left leading to Tias and Macher, park your vehicle and walk northwards for about 400 metres up a wide cinder track through vine fields. Ahead of you is an obvious continuation of the leading edge of the lava field seen at the last stop. Near to the lava front start looking at the boulders of lava within the field walls. Many of them carry very large crystals and aggregates of olivine. Some patches measure as much as 20 centimetres across (Figure 28). **Do not attempt to remove any of these.** When you reach the leading edge proper you can then look for loose fragments of olivine-bearing lava as, indeed, many people appear to have done over the years. They are relatively abundant. Some of these find their way into commercial shops.

By following the lava front round to the left you will, eventually, be able to gain access by a rough track to the upper parts of the lava flow. Once there you can work out that there are three superimposed lava flows each showing solid basalt passing upwards into flow-breccia.

By following the lava front to the right, alongside the stone wall, you eventually come to the slightly obscured contact between the lava flows and the older Pleistocene Volcán de Peña Paloma, which towers above them. This scoria cone is characterised by a mantle of caliche on its north-facing slope and detached blocks and pebbles of this have slid down its ashy flanks.

Figure 28. Olivine-bearing basalt blocks, used locally in walls, La Geria.

Figure 29. Vine pits along the Geria road. Montana Diama in the background.

Now return to the LZ-30 road. By travelling southwestwards towards Uga you will be able to see good examples of the 'enarenado' methodology of cultivating vines and fig trees, by covering the soils with a layer of ash (picón). The circular depressions (gerias) in which the vines are set are very photogenic when viewed *en-masse* (Figure 29).

FURTHER READING

There is a considerable amount of scientific research literature dealing with aspects of the geology of the Canary Islands, but a very large proportion is located within Spanish publications or is written in Spanish. Some of the publications are out of print in any case. It is probable that access to at least some of the literature can be made via the appropriate world-wide web-sites. However, it is generally unnecessary, apart from the connoisseurs of volcanology, to delve into these works in order to gain an appreciation of the volcanic phenomena exposed in Lanzarote. In compiling this guide the following have proved invaluable:

ABDEL-MONEM, A., WATKINS, N. & GAST, P. 1971. K-Ar ages, volcanic stratigraphy and geomagnetic history of the Canary Islands. *American Journal of Science*, **271**, 490-521.

APARICIO, A., ARAÑA, V. & DIEZ GIL, J.L. 1994. Una erupción hidromagmatica en La Isla de Lanzarote: La Caldera de El Cuchillo. (See Garcia & Felpeto, 109-120).

ARAÑA, V. & CARRACEDO, J.C. 1978. *Los Volcanes de Las Canarias* with English text). I. Tenerife, II Lanzarote y Fuertaventura, III Gran Canaria. Editorial Rueda, Madrid.

ARAÑA, V., DIEZ GIL, J.L., ORTIZ, R. & YUGUERO, J. 1984. Convection of the geothermal fluids in the Timanfaya volcanic area (Lanzarote, Canary Islands). *Bulletin of Volcanology*, **47**, 667-677.

ARAÑA, V. 1986. *Journadas Volcanologicas de Lanzarote*. Conference held at Castillo de San Jose, Arrecife, May 1985. 74 pp.

ARAÑA, V. & ORTIZ, R. 1991. The Canary Islands: tectonics, magmatism and geodynamic framework. In: *Magmatism in extensional structural settings*. Springer-Verlag, 209-249.

ARAÑA, V. & BUSTILLO, M.A. 1992. Volcanologic concerns of the siliceous metasedimentary xenoliths included in historic lava flows of Lanzarote, Canary Islands. *Acta Vulcanologica*, **2**, 1-6.

ARAÑA, V. 1994. La Casa de los Volcanes, (See Garcia & Felpeto, 3-29)

ARAÑA, V. 1997. *Casa de Los Volcanes - Jameos del Agua - Tunel del Volcan La Corona - Cueva de los Verdes* Serie Casa de Los Volcanes, No. **6**, 128 pp.

BANDA, E., DAÑOBEITIA, J.J., SURIÑACH, E. & ANSORGE, J. 1981. Features of crustal structure under the Canary Islands. *Earth Planetary and Science Letters*, **55**, 11-24.

CARRACEDO, J.C. & RODRÍGUEZ-BADIOLA, E. 1993. Evolución geologica y magmatica de la isla de Lanzarote (Islas Canarias). *Reviews Academy Canarian Ciencias*, **4**, 25-58.

CARRACEDO, J.C. 1994. The Canary Islands: an example of structural control on the growth of large oceanic-island volcanoes. *Journal of Volcanology and*

Further Reading

Geothermal Research, **60**, 225-241.

COELLO, J., CANTAGREL, J.M., HERNÁN, F., FUSTER, J.M., IBARROLA, E., CASQUET, C., JAMOND, C., DIAZ DE TERÁN, R. & CENDRERO, A. 1992. Evolution of the eastern volcanic ridge of the Canary Islands based on new K-Ar data. *Journal of Volcanology and Geothermal Research*, **53**, 251-274.

FRANCIS, P. 1976. *Volcanoes*. Penguin Books, England, 368 pp.

GARCIA, A. & FELPETO, A. (Eds). 1994. *In Memorium: Dr. Jose Luis Diez Gil.* Serie Casa de Los Volcanes, No.3. Lanzarote. 277 pp. (included 11 papers on Lanzarote).

HERNÁNDEZ-PACHECO, A. & IBARROLA, E. 1973. Geochemical variation trends between the different Canary Island in relation to their geological position. *Lithos*, **6**, 389-402.

HOERNLE, K. & SCHMINCKE, H.U. 1993. The role of partial melting in the 15-Ma geochemical evolution of Gran Canaria: a blob model for the Canary Hotspot. *Journal of Petrology*, **34**, 599-626.

IBARROLA, E. 1969. Variation trends in basaltic rocks of the Canary Islands. *Bulletin of Volcanology*, **3**, 729-777.

LIETZ, J. & SCHMINCKE, H.U. 1975. Mio-Pliocene sea level changes and volcanic episodes on Gran Canaria. *Palaeogeography, Palaeoclimatology and Palaeoecology*, **17**, 214-239.

NEUMANN, E.R. 1991. Ultramafic and mafic xenoliths from Hierro, Canary Islands: evidence for melt infiltration in the upper mantle. *Contributions to Mineralogy and Petrology*, **106**, 236-252.

ROCHFORD, N. 1998. Landscapes of Lanzarote - a countryside guide. Sunflower Books, London, 128 pp.

RODRÍGUEZ-BADIOLA, E., VEINTEMILLAS, S. & CARRACEDO, J.C. 1994. El edificio-isla de Los Ajaches: episodios eruptivos y su evaluacion petrogenetica. (See Garcia & Felpeto, 121-135).

ROMERO, C. 1991. La Erupcion de Timanfaya (Lanzarote 1730-1736). *Serie Informes*, **30**, University La Laguna, Tenerife, 136 pp.

SAGREDO, J. 1969. Origen de las inclusiones de dunitas y ostras rocas ultra basicas en las rocas volcanicas de Lanzarote y Fuerteventura. *Estudios Geologicos*, **25**, 189-233.

SCHMINCKE, H.U. 1982. Volcanic and chemical evolution of the Canary Islands. In: *Geology of the Northwest African Margin*. Springer-Verlag, 273-306.

WILSON, J.T. 1963. A possible origin of the Hawaiian Islands. *Canadian Journal of Physics*, **41**, 863-870. (Reference to Canaries hotspot).

GLOSSARY

Ash, volcanic	Unconsolidated fragments of lava, glass and crystals less than 2 mm in size.
Barranco	A valley, ravine or gully.
Basalt	A black volcanic rock composed of labradorite plagioclase feldspar, pyroxenes and iron ore minerals. In Lanzarote the younger basalts commonly contain green olivine.
Basanite	A basaltic-type rock containing olivine and feldspathoids, such as nepheline.
Caldera	A large volcanic depression, completely or partly walled, more or less circular in plan, the diameter of which is many times that of the included vent or vents.
Caliche	A crust of calcite forming on any kind of rock during weathering and caused by the precipitation of calcium carbonate from evaporating groundwater.
Chilled margins	The borders of an igneous body, such as a dyke, generally finer grained than the main mass due to more rapid cooling.
Columnar jointing	A polygonal pattern of joints at right-angles to cooling surfaces, commonly found in lavas.
Crater	The bowl-shaped mouth of a volcano.
Dunite	An essentially mono-mineralic rock composed of olivine, occurring as enclaves in Lanzarote basalts and volcanic bombs. Derived from the upper mantle.
Dyke	A cross-cutting tabular or sheet-like igneous intrusion with, commonly, a near-vertical attitude. Dykes often act as feeder channels for lava flows.
Gabbro	A coarse grained basic igneous rock consisting of plagioclase feldspar and pyroxenes. Olivine is commonly present. Occurs as enclaves in basaltic volcanic bombs.
Hornito	Steep-sided minor volcanic cones developed on the surface of active lava flows.
Hot spots	Areas on the earth's surface that have a higher than average heat flow. Caused by heating within the mantle giving rise to mantle plumes.
Hydromagmatic	An explosive process when erupting hot lava or magma comes into contact with a body of water, such as the sea (see phreatomagmatic)

Islote	Inliers of ash and lavas totally surrounded by younger ashes and lavas. Commonly in the form of degraded cones and not well-vegetated in Lanzarote.
Lapilli	Volcanic fragments ranging in size from 2-64 mm.
Magma	The molten material generated within the earth and from which igneous rocks are derived.
Marine platform (rasa)	A wave-cut bevelled surface created during periods of raised sea-level.
Mirador	View-point.
Multiple dykes	Compound structures where there has been successive injections of magma of similar composition.
Orogeny	A major period of deformation and mountain-building caused by the collision of tectonic plates.
Palagonite	A yellow to brown, amorphous, altered glass formed by the hydration of fragments of basaltic glass.
Peridotite	A coarse grained ultrabasic igneous rock composed mainly of olivine, with small amounts of pyroxenes sometimes. Feldspar is usually absent. Associated with the upper mantle.
Phenocrysts	Relatively large crystals of a mineral set in a finer grained matrix.
Phreatomagmatic	A violent explosive process when hot lava or magma comes into contact with relatively cold groundwater.
Plate boundary	The edge of a plate where constructive processes may occur by addition of material, or destructive processes where material is destroyed, or conservative where plates slip passively by each other without significant addition or loss of material.
Pyroclastic	Formed of fragments of lava and ash extruded from vents as a result of explosive volcanic eruptions.
Rubefaction	Reddening of rocks due to weathering and the development of iron oxides.
Tectonic plate	A large rigid block formed of continental or oceanic material which moves across the surface of the earth as a result of sea-floor spreading.
Tephra	A collective name for all pyroclastic rocks formed by the ejection of volcanic material.
Trachy-basalt	Basalts containing both plagioclase and potash-rich feldspars, and sometimes showing an internal alignment of the feldspars (flow texture).
Transform fault	A line of fracture oriented at right-angles to mid-oceanic ridges, along which the movements on each side run parallel with the fracture.

Glossary

Vesicular structure — Cavities of various sizes and shapes, though usually small, caused by the entrapment of gases within a cooling lava.

Volcanic tube — A result of the cooling of first the flanks of a lava channel, then secondly its bridging by cooled lava to form a tube. Flow down the tube eventually slows down, then ceases, often leaving an empty space-the tube or tunnel.

Volcanic vent — The subterranean passage or conduit from the underlying magma chamber, through which volcanic products are discharged at the surface.

Notes